KT-117-582

Into The Wild

THOMAS DOCHERTY

OXFORD
UNIVERSITY PRESS

Joe loved **Wild** things.

But he lived in the middle of the city
where there wasn't any *Wild* . . .

Or was there?

When Joe looked outside, the first thing he noticed was the sound of birdsong . . .

and then a light breeze.

Next, a gust of wind blew in a leaf . . .

a twig . . .

seeds . . .

until **the Wild**
grew in Joe's room . . .

and led him out into
the Wild city.

Now he was looking closely, Joe could see that **the Wild** was all around him.

It was up among the branches of the trees...

down between the cracks in the pavement...

and hiding under the bushes.

And the
more Joe
looked,
the more
the Wild
grew . . .

and grew...

and grew.

Until Joe felt completely...

Wild.

The Wild was
MIGHTY.

The Wild was
surprising.

The Wild was
beautiful.

The Wild was
precious.

The Wild was
home.

That night, Joe slept
with **the Wild**
in his heart.

Because **the** *Wild* is
everywhere...

and we are
the Wild too.

The Wild is all around us.

Can you find **Wild things** in your town or city?
They can be in unexpected places. Keep your ears, eyes,
and nose open—you never know what you might discover.